It was Thursday, and the people
thought it was raining.

They were worried that their
giant would get wet.

But when they looked out,
it wasn't rain at all.

The giant was having
a wash in the pond.

The people rushed out with
all the soap and
all the shampoo
they could carry.

The giant took off his shirt and
washed and scrubbed himself.

He ducked his head in the pond.
Then he covered his hair with shampoo.

Bubbles flew everywhere.

The people were slipping and sliding
all over the street.

While the giant was washing
his hair, the people washed his
shirt in the pond.

The children helped.
They took off their socks and shoes
and jumped into the water.

They jumped and jumped on the shirt
until all the dirt came out.

When the shirt was clean,
they climbed into the trees
and hung it out to dry in the sun.

The people brought towels for
the giant to dry himself.

Then they used old sheets to patch
the holes in his shirt.

When he was clean,
the giant looked at the street.
What a mess!

So he blew all the bubbles away.

The children tried to
catch the bubbles.

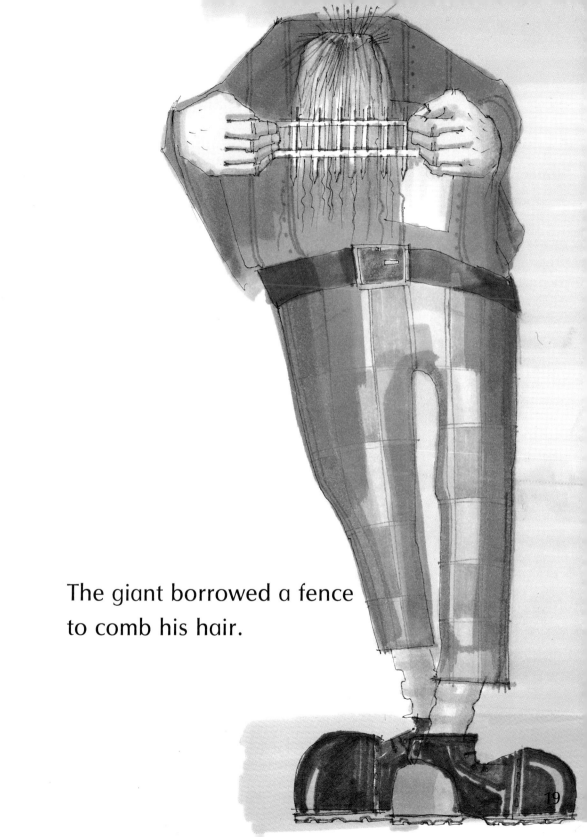

The giant borrowed a fence
to comb his hair.

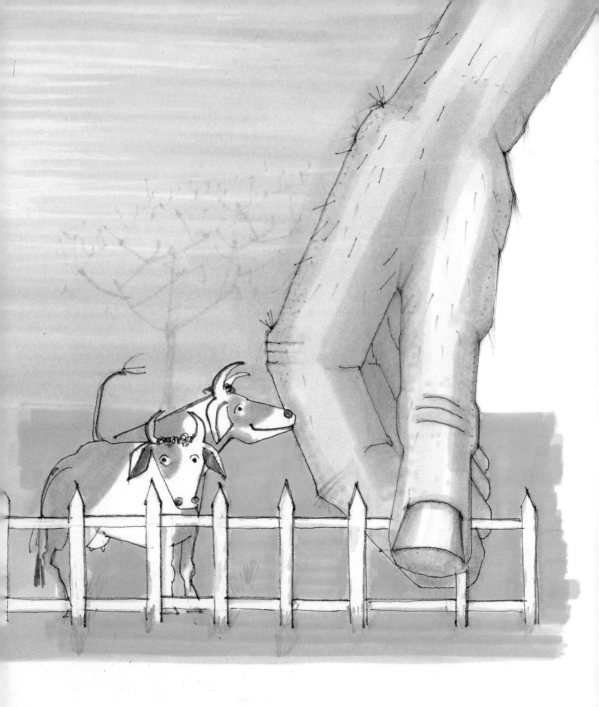

Then he put it back carefully.

He cleaned his boots at the car wash.

Then he looked at himself in the pond.
He smiled.

Everyone was tired.
It had been a busy day of
washing and mending.

The people went home to bed.

"We must think of something special for our giant on Friday," they said as they went to sleep.